top f - normal f no A key
top e - normal take G key
top d - like G but with
B key off.

C000093876

# 100 MORE GRADED FLUTE SOLOS

This publication is not authorised for sale in
the United States of America and/or Canada

**WISE PUBLICATIONS**
*part of The Music Sales Group*

London / New York / Paris / Sydney / Copenhagen / Berlin / Madrid / Tokyo

Published by
**Wise Publications**
14-15 Berners Street, London W1T 3LJ, UK.

Exclusive Distributors:
**Music Sales Limited**
Distribution Centre, Newmarket Road,
Bury St Edmunds, Suffolk IP33 3YB, UK.
**Music Sales Pty Limited**
120 Rothschild Avenue, Rosebery, NSW 2018, Australia.

Order No. AM992475
ISBN 978-1-84772-420-5
This book © Copyright 2008 Wise Publications,
a division of Music Sales Limited.

Unauthorised reproduction of any part of this publication by
any means including photocopying is an infringement of copyright.

Edited by Jenni Wheeler.
Music processed by Camden Music.
Printed in the EU.

**Your Guarantee of Quality**
As publishers, we strive to produce every book to
the highest commercial standards.
This book has been carefully designed to minimise awkward
page turns and to make playing from it a real pleasure.
Particular care has been given to specifying acid-free, neutral-sized
paper made from pulps which have not been elemental chlorine bleached.
This pulp is from farmed sustainable forests and
was produced with special regard for the environment.
Throughout, the printing and binding have been planned to ensure
a sturdy, attractive publication which should give years of enjoyment.
If your copy fails to meet our high standards,
please inform us and we will gladly replace it.

**www.musicsales.com**

## GRADING NOTES

The pieces in this book have been carefully graded according to
various criteria such as rhythmic complexity, phrasing, tempo, key, range, etc.
Look for the number of stars for each piece to give you
an idea of the approximate playing level.
All musicians have particular strengths and weaknesses,
so the grading offered here should be taken as a suggestion only.

Generally, pieces with one star have simple rhythms,
straight forward phrasings and few difficult intervals;
essentially diatonic and in easier keys.

Pieces with two stars will have more challenging passages,
perhaps containing more rhythmic complexity,
more advanced key signatures and possibly explore a wider
range on the intrument.

Three-star pieces may include chromaticism,
challenging articulation and more advanced positioning.
Read through rhythms and keys before playing, and check for
time-signature changes and correct phrasing.

# The Air That I Breathe

Words & Music by Albert Hammond & Mike Hazelwood

© Copyright 1972 Rondor Music (London) Limited.
All rights in Germany administered by Rondor Musikverlag GmbH. All Rights Reserved. International Copyright Secured.

# Against All Odds
## (Take A Look At Me Now)

Words & Music by Phil Collins

© Copyright 1984 Hit & Run Music (Publishing) Limited (75%)/EMI Music Publishing Limited (25%).
All Rights Reserved. International Copyright Secured.

# All These Things That I've Done

Words & Music by Brandon Flowers, Dave Keuning, Mark Stoermer & Ronnie Vannucci

© Copyright 2004 Universal Music Publishing Limited.
All rights in Germany administered by Universal Music Publ. GmbH.
All Rights Reserved. International Copyright Secured.

# Angel

Words & Music by Sarah McLachlan

© Copyright 1997 Sony/ATV Songs LLC/Tyde Music, USA.
Sony/ATV Music Publishing (UK) Limited.
All Rights Reserved. International Copyright Secured.

# America

Words & Music by Johnny Borrell & Andy Burrows

© Copyright 2006 Sony/ATV Music Publishing (UK) Limited.
All Rights Reserved. International Copyright Secured.

15

# Any Dream Will Do
## (from 'Joseph And The Amazing Technicolor® Dreamcoat')

Music by Andrew Lloyd Webber
Lyrics by Tim Rice

© Copyright 1969 The Really Useful Group Limited.
All rights in Germany administered by Universal Music Publ. GmbH.
All Rights Reserved. International Copyright Secured.

# As Time Goes By

Words & Music by Herman Hupfeld

© Copyright 1931 Harms Incorporated, USA.
Redwood Music Limited.
All Rights Reserved. International Copyright Secured.

# Blueberry Hill

Words & Music by Larry Stock, Al Lewis & Vincent Rose

**Moderately**

© Copyright 1940 Chappell & Company Incorporated, USA.
Redwood Music Limited (66.66%)/Chappell Music Limited (33.34%).
All Rights Reserved. International Copyright Secured.

# Cabaret

Words by Fred Ebb
Music by John Kander

© Copyright 1966 Alley Music Company Incorporated/Trio Music Company Incorporated, USA.
Carlin Music Corporation.
All Rights Reserved. International Copyright Secured.

# Can't Help Lovin' Dat Man

Words by Oscar Hammerstein II
Music by Jerome Kern

© Copyright 1927 T.B. Harms & Company Incorporated, USA.
Universal Music Publishing Limited.
All rights in Germany administered by Universal Music Publ. GmbH.
All Rights Reserved. International Copyright Secured.

# Can't Take My Eyes Off You

Words & Music by Bob Crewe & Bob Gaudio

© Copyright 1967 EMI Longitude Music Company/Seasons Four Music Corporation, USA.
EMI Music Publishing Limited (50%)/EMI Music Publishing (WP) Limited (50%).
All Rights Reserved. International Copyright Secured.

# A Case Of You

Words & Music by Joni Mitchell

© Copyright 1971 Joni Mitchell Publishing Corporation, USA.
Sony/ATV Music Publishing (UK) Limited.
All Rights Reserved. International Copyright Secured.

# The Closest Thing To Crazy

Words & Music by Mike Batt

© Copyright 1992 Dramatico Music Publishing Limited.
Sony/ATV Music Publishing (UK) Limited.
All Rights Reserved. International Copyright Secured.

# Coming Around Again

Words & Music by Carly Simon

© Copyright 1987 Famous Music Corporation, USA/C'est Music, USA.
Famous Music Publishing Limited.
All Rights Reserved. International Copyright Secured.

# Constant Craving

### Words & Music by K.D. Lang & Ben Mink

© Copyright 1992 Bumstead Productions/Jane Hathaway's Publishing Company, USA.
Universal Music Publishing Limited (50%)/Rondor Music (London) Limited (50%).
All rights in Germany administered by Universal Music Publ. GmbH.
All rights in Germany administered by Rondor Musikverlag GmbH.
All Rights Reserved. International Copyright Secured.

# Consider Yourself

Words & Music by Lionel Bart

© Copyright 1959 Lakeview Music Publishing Company Limited.
All Rights Reserved. International Copyright Secured.

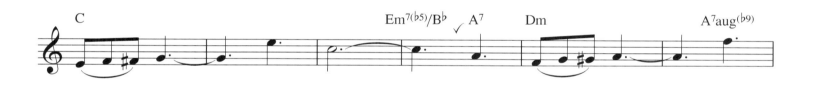

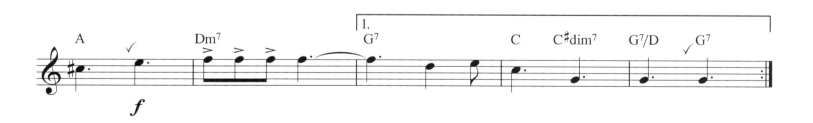

# Cornflake Girl

Words & Music by Tori Amos

© Copyright 1994 Sword And Stone Publishing Company, USA.
All Rights Reserved. International Copyright Secured.

35

# Creep

Words & Music by Thom Yorke, Jonny Greenwood, Colin Greenwood, Ed O'Brien,
Phil Selway, Albert Hammond & Mike Hazelwood

© Copyright 1992 Warner/Chappell Music Limited (66.67%)/Rondor Music (London) Limited (33.33%).
All rights in Germany administered by Rondor Musikverlag GmbH.
All Rights Reserved. International Copyright Secured.

# Corcovado
## (Quiet Nights Of Quiet Stars)

Words & Music by Antonio Carlos Jobim & Giorgio Calabrese

**Smooth latin ballad, with lazy 'late' feel**

© Copyright 1962 & 1965 Universal Music Publishing Limited.
All rights in Germany administered by Universal Music Publ. GmbH.
All Rights Reserved. International Copyright Secured.

# Delilah

Words & Music by Les Reed & Barry Mason

© Copyright 1968 Donna Music Limited.
All Rights Reserved. International Copyright Secured.

# Dancing Queen

Words & Music by Benny Andersson, Stig Anderson & Björn Ulvaeus

© Copyright 1976 Union Songs AB, Sweden.
Bocu Music Limited for Great Britain and the Republic Of Ireland.
All Rights Reserved. International Copyright Secured.

*Repeat and fade*

# Do You Hear The People Sing?

Music by Claude-Michel Schönberg
Original Lyrics by Alain Boublil & Jean-Marc Natel
English Lyrics by Herbert Kretzmer

© Copyright 1980 Editions Musicales Alain Boublil.
Alain Boublil Music Limited (ASCAP).
All Rights Reserved. International Copyright Secured.

# Dreams

Words by Dolores O'Riordan
Music by Dolores O'Riordan & Noel Hogan

© Copyright 1992 Island Music Limited.
Universal/Island Music Limited.
All rights in Germany administered by Universal Music Publ. GmbH.
All Rights Reserved. International Copyright Secured.

# Every Breath You Take

Words & Music by Sting

© Copyright 1983 G M Sumner/EMI Music Publishing Limited, London, WC2H 0QY.
All Rights Reserved. International Copyright Secured.

47

# Everybody's Talkin'

Words & Music by Fred Neil

© Copyright 1967 Coconut Grove Music Company, a division of Third Story Music Company Incorporated, USA.
Carlin Music Corporation.
All Rights Reserved. International Copyright Secured.

*To Coda* ⊕

*D.S. al Coda*

⊕ *Coda*

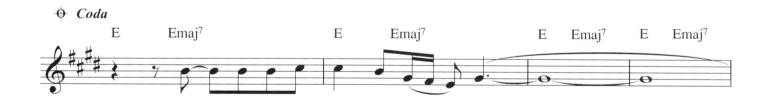

*Repeat and fade*

# Everytime

Words & Music by Britney Spears & Annette Stamatelatos

© Copyright 2003 Zomba Music Publishers Limited (65%)/
Notting Hill Music Limited (28%)/Universal Music Publishing Limited (7%).
All rights in Germany administered by Universal Music Publ. GmbH.
All Rights Reserved. International Copyright Secured.

# Feel

Words & Music by Robbie Williams & Guy Chambers

© Copyright 2003 EMI Music Publishing Limited (50%)/Universal Music Publishing MGB Limited (50%).
All Rights in Germany Administered by Musik Edition Discoton GmbH (A Division of Universal Music Publishing Group).
All Rights Reserved. International Copyright Secured.

# A Fine Romance

Words by Dorothy Fields
Music by Jerome Kern

© Copyright 1936 Universal Music Publishing Limited (50%)/Shapiro Bernstein & Company Limited (50%).
All rights in Germany administered by Universal Music Publ. GmbH.
All Rights Reserved. International Copyright Secured.

# Flying Without Wings

Words & Music by Steve Mac & Wayne Hector

54

© Copyright 1999 Rokstone Music (50%)/Rondor Music (London) Limited (50%).
All rights in Germany administered by Rondor Musikverlag GmbH. All Rights

*To Coda* ⊕

*D.S. al Coda*

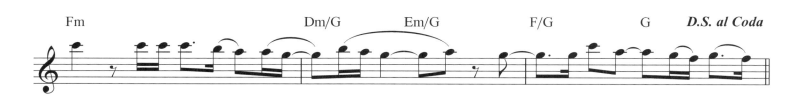

⊕ *Coda*

**rit.**

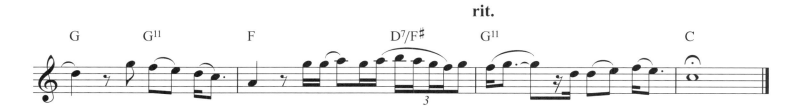

# The Girl From Ipanema
## (Garota De Ipanema)

Music by Antonio Carlos Jobim
English Words by Norman Gimbel
Original Words Vinicius De Moraes

© Copyright 1963 Antonio Carlos Jobim and Vinicius De Moraes, Brazil.
Copyright Renewed 1991 and Assigned to Universal Music Publishing Limited and New Thunder Music, Inc.
English Words Renewed 1991 by Norman Gimbel for the World and Assigned to New Thunder Music, Inc.
Administered by Gimbel Music Group, Inc. (P.O. Box 15221, Beverly Hills, CA 90209-1221 USA).
This arrangement © Copyright 2008 Universal Music Publishing Limited (58.33%) and New Thunder Music, Inc. (41.67%).
All rights in Germany administered by Universal Music Publ. GmbH.
All Rights Reserved. International Copyright Secured.

# Golden Brown

Words & Music by Jet Black, Jean-Jacques Burnel, Hugh Cornwell & David Greenfield

© Copyright 1981 Plumbshaft Limited/Complete Music Limited (75%)/EMI Music Publishing Limited (25%).
All Rights in Germany Administered by Musik Edition Discoton GmbH (A Division of Universal Music Publishing Group).
All Rights Reserved. International Copyright Secured.

# Goodbye Yellow Brick Road

Words & Music by Elton John & Bernie Taupin

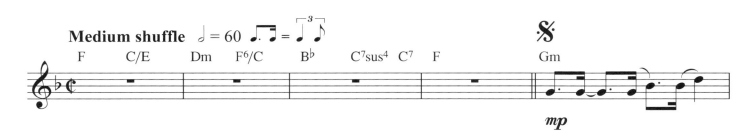

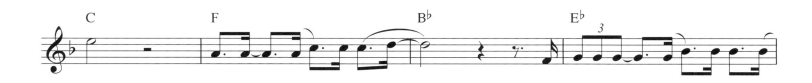

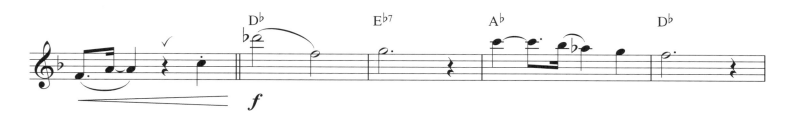

© Copyright 1973 Dick James Music Limited.
Universal/Dick James Music Limited.
All rights in Germany administered by Universal Music Publ. GmbH.
All Rights Reserved. International Copyright Secured.

# God Only Knows

Words & Music by Brian Wilson & Tony Asher

© Copyright 1966 Sea Of Tunes Publishing Company, USA.
Universal Music Publishing Limited.
All rights in Germany administered by Universal Music Publ. GmbH.
All Rights Reserved. International Copyright Secured.

# Grace Kelly

Words & Music by Jodi Marr, Dan Warner, John Merchant & Michael Penniman

© Copyright 2005 Universal Music Publishing Limited (80%)/
Sony/ATV Music Publishing (UK) Limited (10%)/Famous Music Publishing Limited (10%).
All rights in Germany administered by Universal Music Publ. GmbH.
All Rights Reserved. International Copyright Secured.

# Have I Told You Lately

Words & Music by Van Morrison

**Tenderly** ♩ = c.72

© Copyright 1989 Exile Publishing Limited.
Universal Music Publishing Limted.
All rights in Germany administered by Universal Music Publ. GmbH.
All Rights Reserved. International Copyright Secured

# Head Over Feet

Words by Alanis Morissette
Music by Alanis Morissette & Glen Ballard

© Copyright 1995 Music Corporation Of America Incorporated/
Vanhurst PlaceMusic/MCA Music Publishing/Aerostation Corporation, USA.
Universal/MCA Music Limited.
All rights in Germany administered by Universal/MCA Music Publ. GmbH.
All Rights Reserved. International Copyright Secured.

# Here With Me

Words by Dido Armstrong
Music by Dido Armstrong, Pascal Gabriel & Paul Statham

© Copyright 1997 TCF Music Publishing, Inc. and New Enterprises Music, Inc.
This arrangement © Copyright 2008 TCF Music Publishing, Inc. and New Enterprises Music, Inc.
All Rights Controlled and Administered by TCF Music Publishing, Inc.
All Rights Reserved. International Copyright Secured.

# Hopelessly Devoted To You

Words & Music by John Farrar

© Copyright 1978 Ensign Music Corporation/Famous Music Corporation, USA.
All Rights Reserved. International Copyright Secured.

# How Deep Is Your Love

Words & Music by Barry Gibb, Maurice Gibb & Robin Gibb

© Copyright 1977 Crompton Songs.
Gibb Brothers Music (66.66%) Warner/Chappell Music Limited (33.34%).
All Rights Reserved. International Copyright Secured.

# Hung Up

Words & Music by Benny Andersson, Bjorn Ulvaeus, Madonna & Stuart Price

© Copyright 2005 Union Songs AB, Sweden/Bocu Music Limited (50%)/Warner/Chappell Music Limited (50%).
All rights in Germany administered by Universal Music Publ. GmbH.
All Rights Reserved. International Copyright Secured.

# I Can't Stand The Rain

Words & Music by Ann Peebles, Bernard Miller & Don Bryant

© Copyright 1973 Jec Publishing Company, USA.
Universal Music Publishing Limited (75%)/Warner/Chappell Music Limited (25%).
All rights in Germany administered by Universal Music Publ. GmbH.
All Rights Reserved. International Copyright Secured.

# I Don't Want To Miss A Thing

Words & Music by Diane Warren

© Copyright 1998 Realsongs.
Sony/ATV Music Publishing (UK) Limited.
All Rights Reserved. International Copyright Secured.

# The Importance Of Being Idle

Words & Music by Noel Gallagher

© Copyright 2005 Oasis Music (GB).
Sony/ATV Music Publishing (UK) Limited.
All Rights Reserved. International Copyright Secured.

# I Dreamed A Dream

Music by Claude-Michel Schönberg
Original Lyrics by Alain Boublil & Jean-Marc Natel
English Lyrics by Herbert Kretzmer

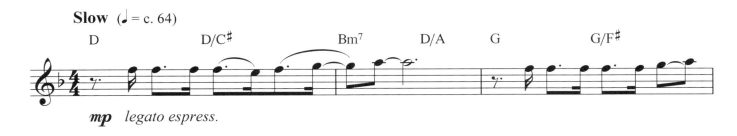

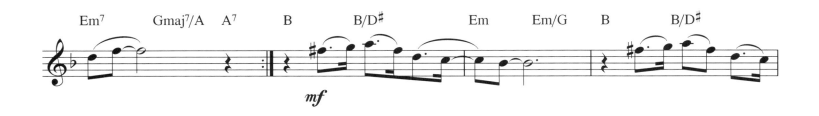

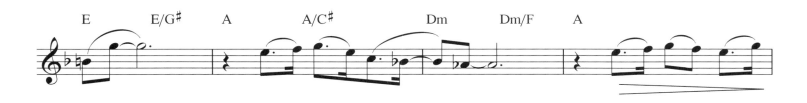

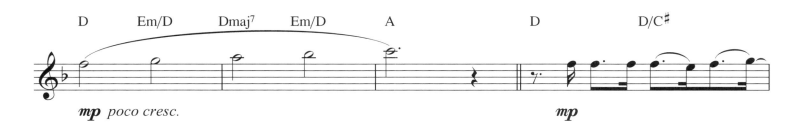

74

© Copyright (Music & Lyrics) 1980 Editions Musicales Alain Boublil.
English Lyrics © Copyright 1985 Alain Boublil Music Limited (ASCAP).
All Rights Reserved. International Copyright Secured.

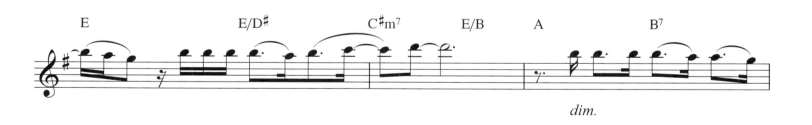

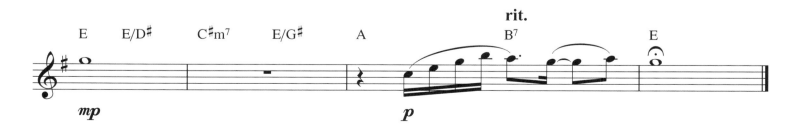

# If You're Not The One

Words & Music By Daniel Bedingfield

© Copyright 2002 Sony/ATV Music Publishing (UK) Limited.
All Rights Reserved. International Copyright Secured.

D.S. al Coda

Coda

77

# In A Sentimental Mood

Words & Music by Duke Ellington, Irving Mills & Manny Kurtz

© Copyright 1935 American Academy of Music Incorporated, USA.
Lafleur Music Limited.
All Rights Reserved. International Copyright Secured.

# Jolene

Words & Music by Dolly Parton

© Copyright 1973 Velvet Apple Music, USA.
Carlin Music Corporation.
All Rights Reserved. International Copyright Secured.

# Kiss From A Rose

Words & Music by Seal

© Copyright 1994 Beethoven Street Music.
Perfect Songs Limited.
All Rights Reserved. International Copyright Secured.

# The Lady Sings The Blues

Words by Billie Holiday
Music by Herbie Nichols

© Copyright 1956 & 1972 Northern Music Company (a division of MCA Incorporated, USA).
Universal/MCA Music Limited.
All rights in Germany administered by Universal/MCA Music Publ. GmbH.
All Rights Reserved. International Copyright Secured.

# Lay Lady Lay

Words & Music by Bob Dylan

© Copyright 1969; Renewed 1997 Big Sky Music.
All Rights Reserved. International Copyright Secured.

# Life On Mars?

Words & Music by David Bowie

© Copyright 1971 Tintoretto Music/RZO Music Limited (37.5%)/
EMI Music Publishing Limited (37.5%)/Chrysalis Music Limited (25%).
All Rights Reserved. International Copyright Secured.

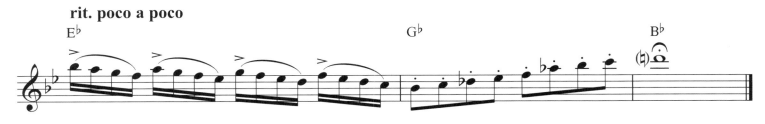

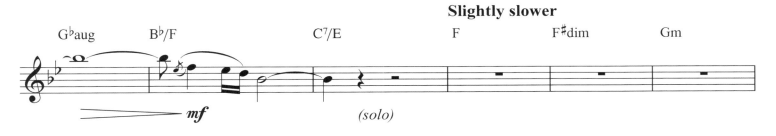

# Live And Let Die

Words & Music by Linda McCartney & Paul McCartney

© Copyright 1973 MPL Communications Limited (75%)/EMI United Partnership Limited (25%).
All Rights Reserved. International Copyright Secured.

# Little Bird

Words & Music by Annie Lennox

© Copyright 1992 La Lennoxa Music Company Limited.
Universal Music Publishing MGB Limited.
All Rights in Germany Administered by Musik Edition Discoton GmbH (A Division of Universal Music Publishing Group).
All Rights Reserved. International Copyright Secured.

# The Long And Winding Road

Words & Music by John Lennon & Paul McCartney

© Copyright 1970 Northern Songs.
All Rights Reserved. International Copyright Secured.

# Love And Affection

Words & Music by Joan Armatrading

© Copyright 1976 Rondor Music (London) Limited.
All rights in Germany administered by Rondor Musikverlag GmbH.
All Rights Reserved. International Copyright Secured.

# Love Me Tender

Words & Music by Elvis Presley & Vera Matson

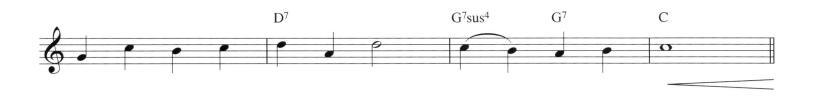

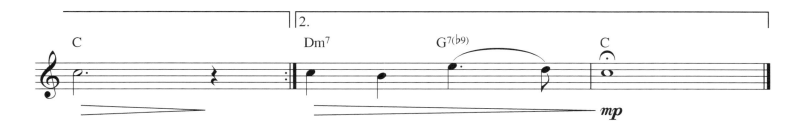

© Copyright 1956 Elvis Presley Music, USA.
Carlin Music Corporation.
All Rights Reserved. International Copyright Secured.

# Lovefool

Words & Music by Peter Svensson & Nina Persson

© Copyright 1996 Stockholm Songs, Sweden.
Universal Music Publishing Limited.
All rights in Germany administered by Universal Music Publ. GmbH.
All Rights Reserved. International Copyright Secured.

# Magic Moments

Words by Hal David
Music by Burt Bacharach

© Copyright 1957 Casa David Music Incorporated.
Famous Music Corporation (50%)/Universal/MCA Music Limited (50%).
All rights in Germany administered by Universal/MCA Music Publ. GmbH.
All Rights Reserved. International Copyright Secured.

# Mother And Child Reunion

Words & Music by Paul Simon

© Copyright 1971 Paul Simon (BMI).
All Rights Reserved. International Copyright Secured.

# A Moment Like This

Words & Music by Jorgen Elofsson & John Reid

© Copyright 2002 Sony/ATV Music Publishing (UK) Limited (50%)/Universal Music Publishing MGB Limited (50%).
All Rights in Germany Administered by Musik Edition Discoton GmbH (A Division of Universal Music Publishing Group).
All Rights Reserved. International Copyright Secured.

# The Music Of The Night
## (from 'The Phantom Of The Opera')

Music by Andrew Lloyd Webber
Lyrics by Charles Hart
Additional Lyrics by Richard Stilgoe

© Copyright 1986 Andrew Lloyd Webber licensed to The Really Useful Group Limited.
All rights in Germany administered by Universal Music Publ. GmbH.
All Rights Reserved. International Copyright Secured.

# My Favourite Things
## (from 'The Sound Of Music')

Words by Oscar Hammerstein
Music by Richard Rodgers

© Copyright 1959 Richard Rodgers & The Estate of Oscar Hammerstein II.
This arrangement © Copyright 2008 Williamson Music Company.
Williamson Music Company owner of arrangement & allied rights throughout the World.
All Rights Reserved. International Copyright Secured.

# My Heart Will Go On
## (Love Theme from 'Titanic')

Words by Will Jennings
Music by James Horner

© Copyright 1997 Famous Music LLC, Ensign Music, TCF Music Publishing, Inc., Fox Film Music Corporation and Blue Sky Rider Songs.
This arrangement © Copyright 2008 TCF Music Publishing, Inc./Fox Film Music Corporation (62.5%)/
Universal Music Publishing Limited (37.5%).
All rights in Germany administered by Universal Music Publ. GmbH.
All Rights Reserved. International Copyright Secured.

# A Night In Tunisia

Words by Raymond Leveen
Music by Frank Paparelli & Dizzy Gillespie

© Copyright 1944 & 1960 MCA Music Publishing (a division of Universal Studios Incorporated, USA).
Universal/MCA Music Limited.
All rights in Germany administered by Universal/MCA Music Publ. GmbH.
All Rights Reserved. International Copyright Secured.

105

# Naive

Words & Music by Luke Pritchard, Hugh Harris, Max Rafferty & Paul Garred

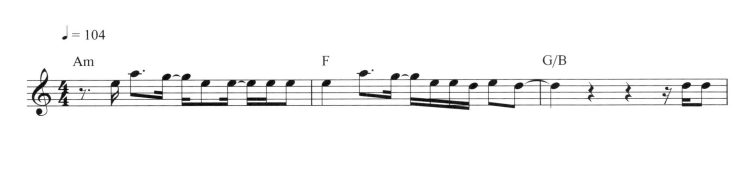

© Copyright 2005 Famous Music Publishing Limited.
All Rights Reserved. International Copyright Secured.

# No Woman, No Cry

Words & Music by Vincent Ford

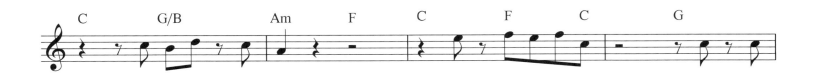

© Copyright 1974 Fifty-Six Hope Road Music Limited/Odnil Music Limited.
Blue Mountain Music Limited.
All Rights Reserved. International Copyright Secured.

(Solo ad lib.)

D.S. al Coda

Coda

Play 3 times

# Nothing Else Matters

Words & Music by James Hetfield & Lars Ulrich

© Copyright 1991 Creeping Death Music, USA.
Universal Music Publishing Limited.
All rights in Germany administered by Universal Music Publ. GmbH.
All Rights Reserved. International Copyright Secured.

# Patience

Words & Music by Mark Owen, Gary Barlow, John Shanks, Jason Orange & Howard Donald

**Moderate pop ballad** ♩ = 88

© Copyright 2006 EMI Music Publishing Limited (33.33%)/Warner/Chappell Music North America (33.33%)/
Sony/ATV Music Publishing (UK) Limited (16.66%)/Universal Music Publishing MGB Limited (16.66%).
All Rights in Germany Administered by Musik Edition Discoton GmbH (A Division of Universal Music Publishing Group).
All Rights Reserved. International Copyright Secured.

*cresc. poco a poco*

# Petite Fleur (Little Flower)

Music by Sidney Bechet

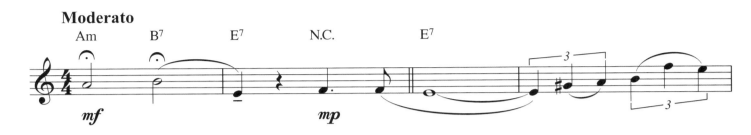

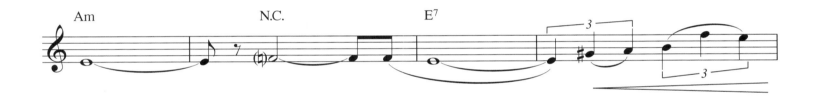

© Copyright 1952 & 1959 Les Editions Musicales du Carrousel, France.
TRO Essex Music Limited.
All Rights Reserved. International Copyright Secured.

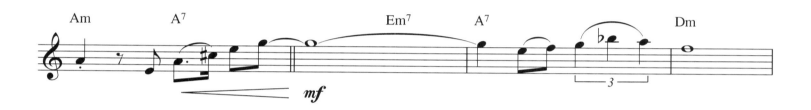

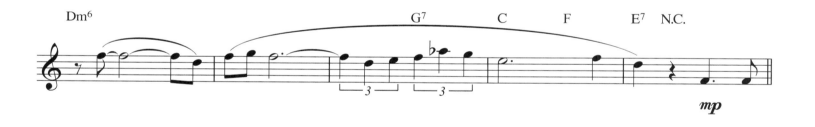

# Play Dead

Words & Music by David Arnold, Bjork Gudmundsdottir & John Wardle

© Copyright 1993 Neue Welt Musikverlag GmbH.
Warner/Chappell Music Limited (66.66%)/Universal Music Publishing Limited (33.34%).
All rights in Germany administered by Universal Music Publ. GmbH.
All Rights Reserved. International Copyright Secured.

# Purple Rain

### Words & Music by Prince

© Copyright 1984 Controversy Music, USA.
Universal/MCA Music Limited.
All rights in Germany administered by Universal/MCA Music Publ. GmbH.
All Rights Reserved. International Copyright Secured.

# Round Round

Words & Music by Nick Coler, Brian Higgins, Keisha Buchanan, Mutya Buena, Heidi Range, Florian Pflueger,
Felix Stecher, Robin Hofmann, Miranda Cooper, Timothy Powell, Lisa Cowling & Rino Spadavecchia

© Copyright 2002 Universal Music Publishing Limited (48.34%)/
Warner/Chappell Music Limited (35%)/EMI Music Publishing Limited (16.66%).
All rights in Germany administered by Universal Music Publ. GmbH.
All Rights Reserved. International Copyright Secured.

# Ruby

Words & Music by Nicholas Hodgson, Richard Wilson, Andrew White, James Rix & Nicholas Baines

© Copyright 2006 Imagem Music Limited.
All Rights Reserved. International Copyright Secured.

# The Scientist

Words & Music by Guy Berryman, Chris Martin, Jon Buckland & Will Champion

© Copyright 2002 BMG Music Publishing Limited.
Universal Music Publishing MGB Limited.
All Rights in Germany Administered by Musik Edition Discoton GmbH (A Division of Universal Music Publishing Group).
All Rights Reserved. International Copyright Secured.

# She Will Be Loved

Words & Music by Adam Levine, James Valentine, Jesse Carmichael, Mickey Madden & Ryan Dusick

© Copyright 2002 February Twenty Second Music, USA.
Universal Music Publishing MGB Limited.
All Rights in Germany Administered by Musik Edition Discoton GmbH (A Division of Universal Music Publishing Group).
All Rights Reserved. International Copyright Secured.

# Theme From The Simpsons™
## (from the Twentieth Century Fox Television Series 'The Simpsons')

Music by Danny Elfman

© Copyright 1990, 1991 Fox Film Music Corporation.
This arrangement © Copyright 2008 Fox Film Music Corporation.
All Rights Reserved. International Copyright Secured.

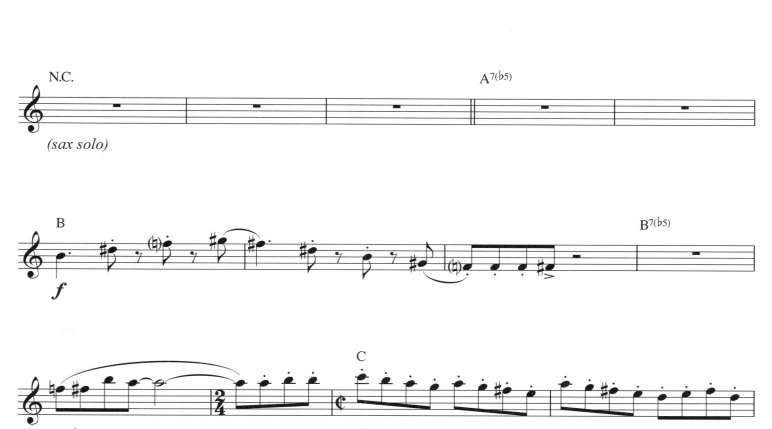

(sax solo)

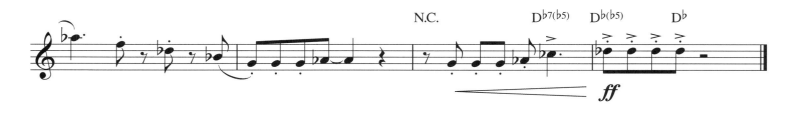

# Sing

Words & Music by Fran Healy

© Copyright 2001 Sony/ATV Music Publishing (UK) Limited.
All Rights Reserved. International Copyright Secured.

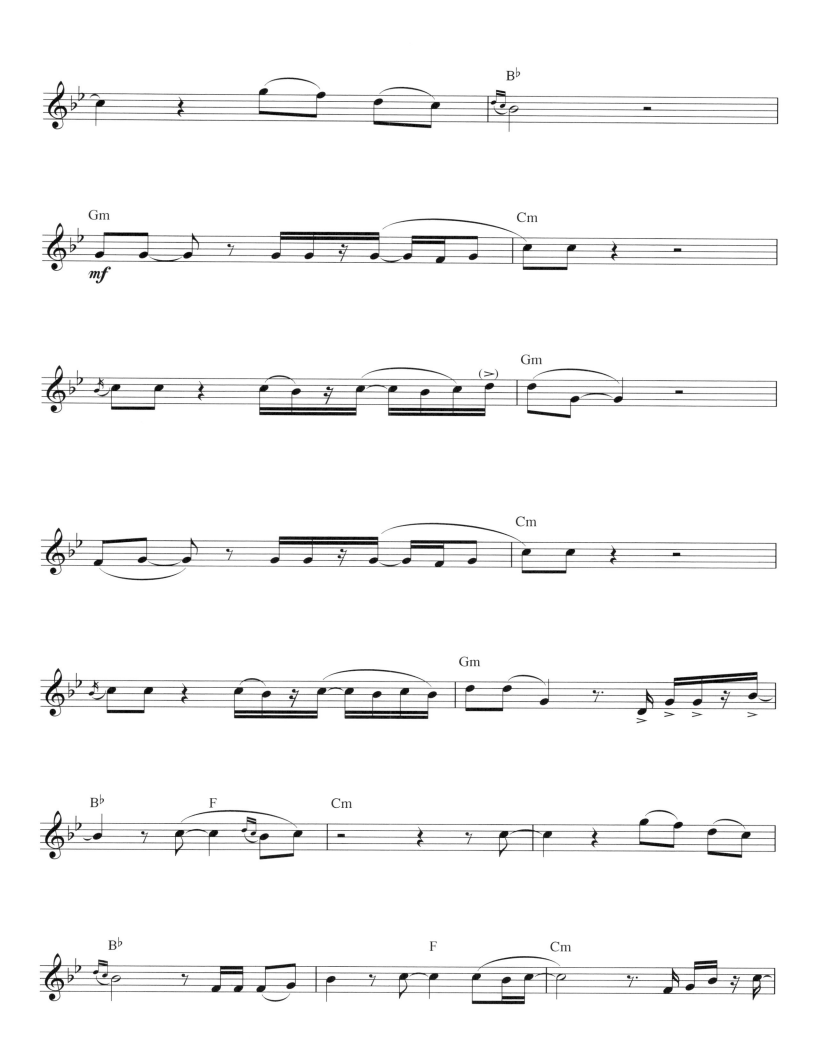

# Smoke Gets In Your Eyes

Words by Otto Harbach
Music by Jerome Kern

© Copyright 1934 T.B. Harms & Company Incorporated, USA.
Universal Music Publishing Limited.
All rights in Germany administered by Universal Music Publ. GmbH.
All Rights Reserved. International Copyright Secured.

# Smile

Words & Music by Jackie Mittoo, Clement Dodd, Iyiola Babalola, Darren Lewis & Lily Allen

130

© Copyright 2006 Universal Music Publishing Limited (50%)/Sparta Florida Music Group Limited (50%).
All rights in Germany administered by Universal Music Publ. GmbH.
All Rights Reserved. International Copyright Secured.

131

# Somethin' Stupid

### Words & Music by C. Carson Parks

© Copyright 1967 Greenwood Music Company, USA.
Montclare Music Company Limited.
All Rights Reserved. International Copyright Secured.

# Sunday Morning

Words & Music by Lou Reed & John Cale

© Copyright 1966 Oakfield Avenue Music Limited/John Cale Music Incorporated, USA.
Screen Gems-EMI Music Limited (50%)/Universal/Island Music Limited (50%).
All rights in Germany administered by Universal Music Publ. GmbH.
All Rights Reserved. International Copyright Secured.

# Songbird

Words & Music by Christine McVie

© Copyright 1977 Fleetwood Mac Music, USA.
Universal Music Publishing MGB Limited.
All Rights in Germany Administered by Musik Edition Discoton GmbH (A Division of Universal Music Publishing Group).
All Rights Reserved. International Copyright Secured.

# Suddenly I See

Words & Music by KT Tunstall

136

© Copyright 2004 Sony/ATV Music Publishing (UK) Limited.
All Rights Reserved. International Copyright Secured.

# Take Five

Music by Paul Desmond

© Copyright 1960 & 1961 Derry Music Company, USA.
The Valentine Music Group Limited.
All Rights Reserved. International Copyright Secured.

# Teardrop

Words & Music by Robert Del Naja, Grant Marshall, Andrew Vowles & Elizabeth Fraser

**With a heavy beat** ♩ = 76

© Copyright 1998 Universal/Island Music Limited (50%)/Sony/ATV Music Publishing (UK) Limited (50%).
All rights in Germany administered by Universal/MCA Music Publ. GmbH.
All Rights Reserved. International Copyright Secured.

# Take My Breath Away

Words by Tom Whitlock
Music by Giorgio Moroder

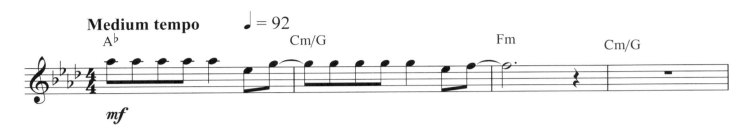

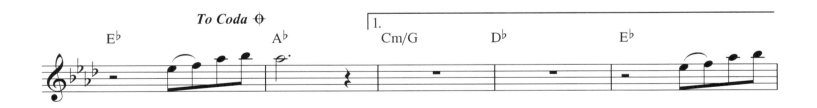

© Copyright 1986 Budde Music Incorporated.
Famous Music Publishing Limited (50%)/Warner/Chappell Music North America (50%).
All Rights Reserved. International Copyright Secured.

141

# (They Long To Be) Close To You

Words by Hal David
Music by Burt Bacharach

© Copyright 1963 Casa David Music Incorporated/New Hidden Valley Music Company, USA.
Universal/MCA Music Limited (50%)/P & P Songs Limited (50%).
All rights in Germany administered by Universal/MCA Music Publ. GmbH.
All Rights Reserved. International Copyright Secured.

# This Year's Love

Words & Music by David Gray

© Copyright 1998 Chrysalis Music Limited.
All Rights Reserved. International Copyright Secured.

# A Time For Us
## (from 'Romeo And Juliet'- Love Theme)

Music by Nino Rota

© Copyright 1968 Famous Music Corporation, USA.
All Rights Reserved. International Copyright Secured.

# Umbrella

Words & Music by Christopher Stewart, Terius Nash, Shawn Carter & Thaddis Harrell

**Moderate** ♩ = 85

© Copyright 2007 Warner/Chappell Music Limited (40%)/Peermusic (UK) Limited (40%)/
EMI Music Publishing Limited (10%)/Sony/ATV Music Publishing (UK) Limited (10%).
All Rights Reserved. International Copyright Secured.

# Where Do I Begin
## (Theme from 'Love Story')

Words by Carl Sigman
Music by Francis Lai

© Copyright 1970 Famous Music Publishing Limited (50%)/Campbell Connelly & Company Limited (50%).
All Rights Reserved. International Copyright Secured.

# Wires

Words & Music by Joel Pott, Carey Willetts, Steve Roberts & Tim Wanstall

© Copyright 2003 Chrysalis Music Limited
All Rights Reserved. International Copyright Secured.

# Wild World

Words & Music by Cat Stevens

© Copyright 1970 Salafa Limited.
All Rights Reserved. International Copyright Secured.

# Will You

Words by Hazel O'Connor
Music by Wesley Magoogan & Hazel O'Connor

© Copyright 1980 Complete Music Limited (75%)/EMI Music Publishing Limited (25%).
All Rights Reserved. International Copyright Secured.

# Wisemen

Words & Music by James Hogarth, Sacha Skarbek & James Blunt

© Copyright 2004 EMI Music Publishing Limited (50%)/Bucks Music Group Limited (25%)/Universal Music Publishing MGB Limited (25%).
All Rights in Germany Administered by Musik Edition Discoton GmbH (A Division of Universal Music Publishing Group).
All Rights Reserved. International Copyright Secured.

# With A Little Help From My Friends

Words & Music by John Lennon & Paul McCartney

© Copyright 1967 Northern Songs.
Sony/ATV Music Publishing (UK) Limited.
All Rights Reserved. International Copyright Secured.

# With Or Without You

Words & Music by U2

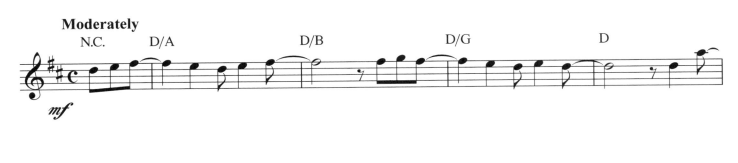

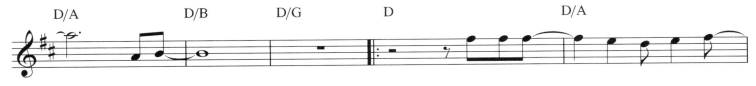

© Copyright 1987 Blue Mountain Music Limited/Mother Music Limited/PolyGram International Music Publishing B.V.
All rights in Germany administered by Universal Music Publ. GmbH.
All Rights Reserved. International Copyright Secured.

# You Give Me Something

Words & Music by Francis White & James Morrison

**Sweetly, with passion** ♩ = 80

© Copyright 2006 Sony/ATV Music Publishing (UK) Limited (50%)/Universal Music Publishing Limited (50%).
All Rights in Germany administered by Universal Music Publ. GmbH.
All Rights Reserved. International Copyright Secured.

# Wonderful Tonight

Words & Music by Eric Clapton

© Copyright 1977, 1999 & 2004 Eric Clapton.
All Rights Reserved. International Copyright Secured.